PLANTS AND TREES
INSTRUCTIONS

1 Open the front flap on the VR viewer. Bring the top and side flaps up and over. The slide flaps attach to the side of the viewer with Velcro.

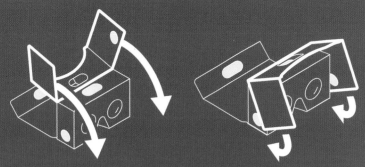

2 Download PI VR Plants and Trees, available on the App Store or Google Play. Direct links to the store locations are found at: pilbooks.com/PIVRPlantsandTrees.

3 Launch the app. You may be asked to calibrate your viewer by scanning the QR code found on the bottom of the viewer itself. You will be able to change your viewer settings later in the options menu.

4 After calibrating your viewer, you will be prompted to scan the QR code found to the right to verify your possession of this book.

5 You will see a double image of a deciduous forest on your phone. Insert your smartphone into the front compartment of the VR viewer. The line between the two images should line up with the notch at the center point of the viewer, between the two lenses. If your screen seems blurry, make sure the smartphone is aligned precisely with the center of the viewer. Adjusting the phone left or right a few millimeters can make a big difference. The tilt of the viewer and the phone can also affect how the screen looks to you.

6 Look around to explore! PI VR Plants and Trees does not require a lever or remote control. You control each interaction with your gaze. When you see a loading circle, keep your gaze focused until it loads fully to access videos, slideshows, and games.

7 Gaze at the X to close out of video, slideshow, or game screens.

Loading

Exit

pi

Publications International, Ltd.

Get the App!

This book is enhanced by an app that can be downloaded from the App Store or Google Play*. Apps are available to download at no cost. Once you've downloaded the app to your smartphone**, use the QR code found on page 1 of this book to access an immersive, 360° virtual reality environment. Then slide the phone into the VR viewer and you're ready to go.

Compatible Operating Systems

- Android 4.1 (JellyBean) or later

- iOS 8.0 or later

Compatible Phones

The app is designed to work with smartphones with a screen size of up to 6 inches. Removing your device from its case may provide a better fit in the viewer. If your smartphone meets the above operating system requirements and has gyroscope functionality it should support GoogleVR. Publications International, Ltd. has developed and tested this software with the following devices:

- Google Nexus 5X, Google Nexus 6

- Motorola Moto Z

- Apple iPhone 6 Plus, Apple iPhone 8, Apple iPhone XR

- Samsung Galaxy S6, Samsung Galaxy S7, Samsung Galaxy S8, Samsung Galaxy S9

Caution

The viewer should not be exposed to moisture or extreme temperatures. The viewer is not water resistant. It is potentially combustible if the lenses are left facing a strong light source.

Cover art from Shutterstock.com.

Interior art from Encyclopædia Britannica, Inc. and Shutterstock.com.

App content from Encyclopædia Britannica, Inc., Filament Games, and Shutterstock.com.

Louis Weber, CEO
Publications International, Ltd.
8140 Lehigh Avenue
Morton Grove, IL 60053

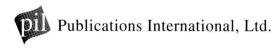

For inquiries email: customer_service@pubint.com

ISBN: 978-1-64030-781-0

Manufactured in China.

8 7 6 5 4 3 2 1

*We reserve the right to terminate the apps.
**Smartphone not included. Standard data rates may apply to download. Once downloaded, the app does not use data or require Wi-Fi access.

CONTENTS

INTRODUCTION

Wherever there is sunlight, air, and soil, plants can be found. On the northernmost coast of Greenland, the Arctic poppy peeps out from beneath the ice. Mosses and tussock grasses grow in Antarctica. Flowers of vivid color and great variety force their way up through the snow on mountainsides. Many shrubs and cacti thrive in deserts that go without rain for years at a time, and rivers, lakes, and swamps are filled with water plants.

FIVE FAST FACTS

1. To date, more than 300,000 plant species have been identified and described.

2. Botanists—the scientists who study plants—estimate that there are tens of thousands of unidentified species yet to be discovered, especially in less explored ecosystems such as tropical forests.

3. Most of the energy consumed in terrestrial ecosystems is provided by plants, and as a consequence, land animals are dependent on them for their food.

4. Plants absorb minerals, such as potassium and phosphorus, from the soil. These are stored in plant tissues and are an essential part of the diet of animals that eat plants.

5. Plants, unlike many animals and protozoans, cannot move about freely by their own efforts.

Arctic poppy in Iceland

The American aloe, or century plant, typically lives for more than a decade while its stem and leaves grow. Eventually, the plant produces an enormous flowering stalk up to 40 feet (12 meters) tall. After the flowers mature and seeds are produced, the plant soon dies.

Plants are capable of certain kinds of movement, such as turning toward light and reaching toward water, but not of moving themselves from place to place.

USE THE VR VIEWER AND ASSOCIATED APP
Enhance your experience by using the app! Put your smartphone in the VR viewer to see a forest in all four seasons.

WHAT IS A PLANT?

Exactly what is a plant and how is it different from other life-forms? This may initially seem like a simple question. Everyone knows that an elm tree is a plant, whereas a dog is not. Nevertheless, the precise definition of plants is still a matter of debate among some scientists.

WHAT SCIENTISTS ONCE THOUGHT

As recently as the late 1960s, scientists believed that all organisms could be classified as members of either the plant or the animal kingdom. Life-forms that are green and that can synthesize their own food using light energy were put in the plant kingdom. Those organisms that lack green pigment and are able to move about were considered to be animals. As scientists made more detailed studies of certain organisms that were considered to be plants, they recognized that they were very different from plants and that they did not share an evolutionary history with them.

Algae are members of the kingdom Protista, not Plantae.

Mushrooms are members of the kingdom Fungi, not Plantae.

WHAT SCIENTISTS THINK TODAY

Today plants are recognized as multicellular organisms that have cells with cell walls composed of cellulose, a rigid complex carbohydrate. Cellulose is the material that lends stiffness to tree trunks, twigs, and the veins of leaves. Most plants can carry out photosynthesis. This activity takes place in special structures, or organelles, called chloroplasts and makes use of a green chemical compound called chlorophyll. Plants are eukaryotes—that is, their cells contain a true nucleus and other membrane-bound bodies. This property distinguishes plants from bacteria and archaea.

CLASSIFICATION

Plants may be organized according to the forms in which they grow. They can also be classified according to the length of their life cycles or in terms of their complexity and evolutionary ancestry. A common classification scheme is based on growth form.

TREES

Plants are called trees if they have tall, woody stems, or trunks, and are generally 8 feet (2.4 meters) or more in height when mature.

On one summer day a medium-sized apple tree soaks up about 800 pounds, or 94 gallons (356 liters), of water. Leaf pores then release about 96 percent of the water to the air. The leaves use only about 4 percent for making food. Thus forests act as reservoirs of rainwater, whereas deforested regions are subject to floods and erosion.

SHRUBS

Shrubs are low, woody plants, usually with many stems branching off close to the ground. When many-branched and dense, they may be called bushes. Thousands of varieties of shrubs are cultivated by gardeners, either as ornamentals or, in some cases, for their edible fruits. Some flowering shrubs are considered so handsome that they are planted alone or in small mixed groups.

Daphnes, forsythias, and rhododendrons like this one are popular flowering shrubs.

Marjoram, an herb

HERBS

Herbs have tender, juicy stems in which the woody tissue is much less developed than it is in shrubs and trees.

VARIETY

Within each of these groups there is a great deal of variety. For example, some trees, such as the giant sequoia, can grow to heights of more than 300 feet (90 meters), whereas others, such as the flowering dogwood, rarely grow to more than 30 feet (9 meters) in height.

FLOWER PLANT CLASSIFICATION

Flowering plants may be divided into three groups, according to the length and pattern of their life cycles.

ANNUALS

Annuals complete their life cycle in a single year. The seeds sprout, or germinate, the seedlings develop into flowering plants, new seeds are produced, and the parent plant dies—all in a single growing season. Annual plants often grow in habitats that are inhospitable during part of the year. They survive through these inhospitable periods in the form of seeds, which can withstand environmental extremes. Many familiar garden flowers are annuals.

Canterbury bells are biennials, as are many common garden flowers, including foxgloves, hollyhocks, and English daisies.

All the common garden perennials, including peonies, irises, and phlox (pictured), were developed from wild species.

BIENNIALS

Biennials require two years to complete their life cycle. In the first year they produce stems and leaves; in the second year they produce blossoms and seeds and then die. During the first year they produce through photosynthesis the food reserves that they need to produce their flowers and seeds the following year.

PERENNIALS

Perennials live for more than two years. Wildflowers are perennial plants. Some perennials produce flowers and seeds throughout their lives. Others, however, produce flowers only once and then die. After the flowers mature and seeds are produced, the plant soon dies.

Most perennials are annual above ground—that is, their stems, leaves, and blossoms die in the fall. These plants, however, survive through the winter by means of their underground roots and stems. Trees, shrubs, and herbs also live and grow in much the same way.

Zinnia are perennial where they are native—from the southern United States to Chile, being especially abundant in Mexico—but are annual elsewhere.

FROM SIMPLE TO COMPLEX

Scientists organize the plant kingdom into divisions that are arranged in order from the simplest to the most complex. The plant divisions can be arranged into three main groups on the basis of differences in the structure of the plant bodies. These groups are the nonvascular plants, seedless vascular plants, and vascular seed plants.

Hornwart

NONVASCULAR PLANTS

The first land plants were the liverworts, hornworts, and mosses. These nonvascular land plants first grew more than 450 million years ago. Although plants belonging to these three divisions are able to grow on land and are more complex than most algae, they lack the specialized tissues for transporting water and food that are found in more developed plants, and they do not make seeds.

Ferns

SEEDLESS VASCULAR PLANTS

Seedless vascular plants—ferns and their relatives—are plants that have specialized tissues for conducting water and food but that do not reproduce by means of seeds. They first appeared on dry land more than 400 million years ago. Seedless vascular plants include the club mosses, horsetails, and ferns. These plants have stems, roots, and leaves that are similar to those of higher plants. They do not produce flowers, however; they reproduce by means of spores.

VASCULAR SEED PLANTS

Vascular seed plants, which include conifers and flowering plants, have transport tissues and produce seeds. Seed plants evolved more than 300 million years ago. Seed plants include five divisions: the cycads, the ginkgo, the conifers, the gnetophytes, and the flowering plants. The first four groups are often called gymnosperms, a name that refers to the fact that their seeds lie naked, or exposed, on the scales of cones. Flowering plants are often called angiosperms—their seeds are protected inside a fruit.

Cycads are found only in wet tropical forests. These plants resemble palm trees.

Gnetophytes have many structural features that resemble those of flowering plants, but they have naked seeds.

Ginkgo trees

PARTS OF PLANTS

A plant is actually more complex than it might appear. Its various parts, composed of specialized cells and tissues, work together to carry on the plant's life functions. The leaves gather sunlight and help the plant make its food; the stems support the plant; the roots anchor the plant and draw water and minerals from the soil; the flowers, fruits, and seeds play a role in the plant's reproduction.

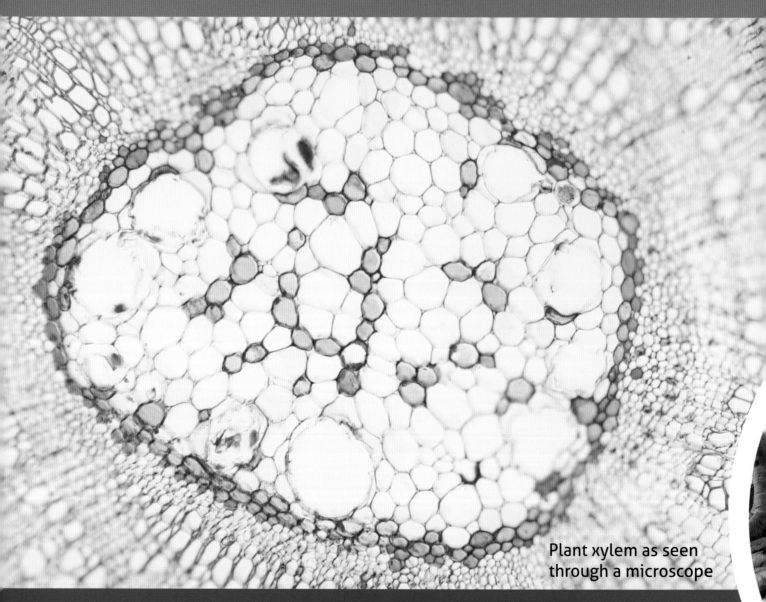

Plant xylem as seen through a microscope

VASCULAR TISSUES

Vascular tissues are specialized for the transport of materials throughout the plant body. They include two types of complex tissue: xylem, which carries water and dissolved minerals, and phloem, which carries food in the form of sugary sap.

LEAVES

Plants may well be thought of as food factories. The most important part of the plant factory is the chemical laboratory—the leaves. Within the cells of the leaves the chlorophyll-containing organelles called chloroplasts carry out photosynthesis. All life on Earth depends on photosynthesis.

Chloroplast

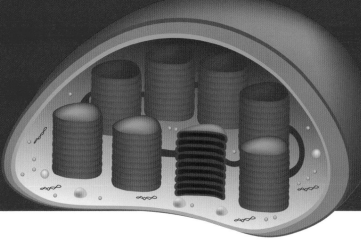

STEMS

Stems give the plant support. The xylem and phloem within the stem distribute the water and sap throughout the plant. Leaves, flowers, and branches develop from buds on the stem.

ROOTS

The roots may be called the receiving rooms of the plant factory, for one of their chief functions is to draw water and minerals from the soil. As rainwater filters into the ground, it dissolves the minerals in the soil. The plant uses this solution for its work in making food. Roots also anchor the plant in the soil and serve as places to store food.

PLANT REPRODUCTION

Plants reproduce, or make more of their kind, either by seeds or spores. Seeds and spores are small structures that develop on plants and then fall off. They then may grow into new plants. Seeds are larger and more complex than spores.

FLOWERS AND FRUITS

Most vascular plants reproduce by seeds. Most seed-bearing plants grow flowers. Fruits grow from the flowers, and seeds grow inside the fruits.

CONES

Other vascular plants do not grow flowers or fruits. For example, the plants called conifers form their seeds inside cones. Conifers include pines, spruces, firs, and similar trees and shrubs.

SPORES

Nonvascular plants reproduce by spores. A few kinds of vascular plants, such as ferns, also reproduce by spores.

VEGETATIVE REPRODUCTION

Sometimes plants can reproduce without spores or seeds. Stems, leaves, or other parts of a plant may grow into new plants. For instance, strawberry plants grow runners, or stems that creep along the ground. These stems may form roots and grow into new plants. This process is called vegetative reproduction.

CUTTINGS

Cuttings, also called slips, are twigs, branches, or leaves cut from the parent plant and placed in soil, sand, or water. In time, new roots, stems, and leaves grow from the cuttings. The willow tree, geranium, begonia, and African violet are examples of plants that may be produced in this way.

PHOTOSYNTHESIS

Photosynthesis is the process in which green plants use sunlight to make their own food. Photosynthesis is necessary for life on Earth. Without it there would be no green plants, and without green plants there would be no animals.

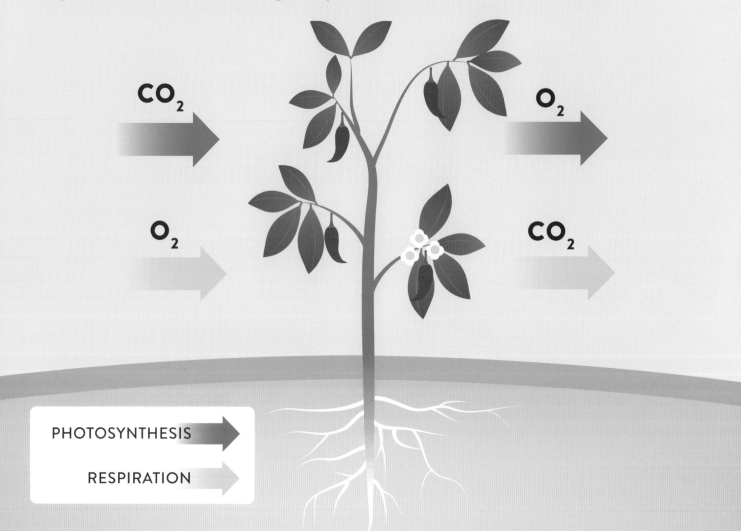

WHAT DOES PHOTOSYNTHESIS NEED?

Photosynthesis requires sunlight, chlorophyll, water, and carbon dioxide gas. Chlorophyll is a substance in all green plants, especially in the leaves. Plants take in water from the soil and carbon dioxide from the air.

HOW DOES PHOTOSYNTHESIS WORK?

Photosynthesis starts when chlorophyll absorbs energy from sunlight. Green plants use this light energy to change water and carbon dioxide into oxygen and nutrients called sugars. The plants use some of the sugars and store the rest. The oxygen is released into the air.

WHY IS PHOTOSYNTHESIS IMPORTANT?

Photosynthesis is very important because almost all living things depend on plants for food. Photosynthesis is also important because of the oxygen it produces. Humans and other animals need to breathe in oxygen to survive.

NOT JUST PLANTS

Some living things other than plants also make their own food through photosynthesis. They include certain types of bacteria and algae.

CELLULAR RESPIRATION

To make cellulose, to build new cells, to store a reserve food supply, and to carry on all other activities necessary for living and growing, a plant needs energy. Energy is obtained by "burning" some of the glucose, a simple sugar produced during photosynthesis.

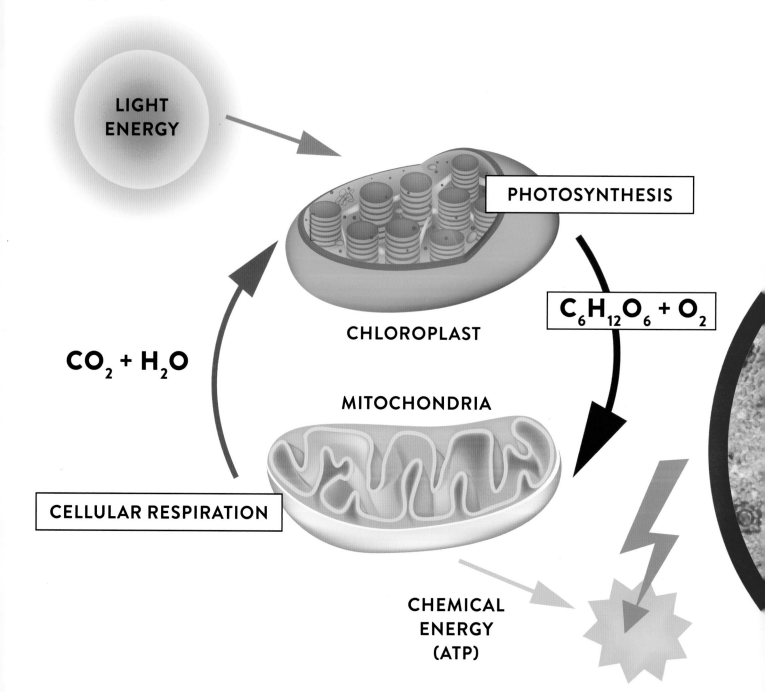

LIGHT ENERGY

PHOTOSYNTHESIS

CHLOROPLAST

$C_6H_{12}O_6 + O_2$

$CO_2 + H_2O$

MITOCHONDRIA

CELLULAR RESPIRATION

CHEMICAL ENERGY (ATP)

GLUCOSE AND OXYGEN

Just as coal releases energy when it burns in the presence of oxygen, so glucose and oxygen react together to release energy. The glucose is not burned in a fire, as is the case in a coal furnace, but through the chemical process known as cellular respiration. Cellular respiration is sometimes called aerobic respiration because it takes place in the presence of oxygen (the root aer- comes from the Greek word meaning "air"). Cellular respiration goes on day and night in every cell in a plant.

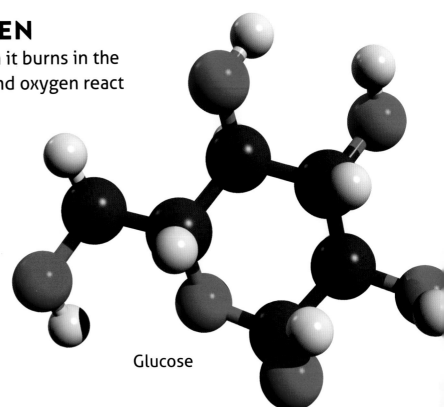

Glucose

Stomata in leaves

A CONSTANT PROCESS

The chemical reactions involved in cellular respiration are the reverse of those involved in photosynthesis. In cellular respiration, oxygen enters the plant through the stomata, or small openings, of the leaves, through the roots (either from air spaces in the soil or in solution in water), and through the air openings in the stems. Glucose is broken down in the presence of oxygen, releasing chemical energy and producing carbon dioxide and water as waste products. The glucose is thus turned back into the same two substances from which it was made during photosynthesis, and the carbon dioxide and water vapor are released back into the air through the stomata.

PLANTS AND WINTER

In summer, plants make and store food in their roots, stems, or seeds. In winter, they rest. Plants pass the winter in various ways.

ANNUALS
Annuals flower in the same season that they are planted. Then, transferring all their reserve food to their seeds, the plants wither and die. Inside the protective seed covering, the embryonic plant lies dormant until the moisture and warmth of spring stimulate its growth.

BIENNIELS

Biennials form only leaves and buds during the first season and store food in their underground roots. The upper parts die in the winter. During the following season the reserve food from the roots is used to make new stems, which bear flowers and seeds. In the second winter the plants die. Their seeds produce a new generation in the spring.

A maple tree begins to bud in springtime.

PERENNIALS

In cold climates perennials store food in their roots or stems and rest during the winter. In warm climates they simply continue growing. Trees and shrubs shed their leaves and for the winter form an insulating jacket of waxy scales on the buds from which new growth will appear the next year.

HARDENING

As the days grow shorter and the nights grow longer and colder, the food substances stored in the leaves of perennial plants flow back into the twigs, branches, and trunk. The gradual decrease in temperature causes changes in the plant tissues that make them more resistant to cold. This preparation for the upcoming winter months is called hardening.

WHY LEAVES CHANGE COLORS

When the chlorophyll decomposes chemically and becomes colorless, the leaves take on their autumn colors of yellow, red, and orange. These colors are caused by the presence of pigments other than chlorophyll. Many of them are always present, but during the summer there is so much more chlorophyll that these colors are masked.

PLANTS AND ECOSYSTEMS

Plants are vital parts of nearly all terrestrial ecosystems. In ecosystems, energy is cycled through food chains. Plants trap light energy during photosynthesis and store it as chemical energy. That energy is then obtained by organisms (herbivores) that eat plants and use the energy to grow and reproduce. Herbivores, in turn, are the primary energy source for carnivores—organisms that eat animals.

WHAT ABOUT AQUATIC ECOSYSTEMS?

In aquatic ecosystems, algae play a role similar to that of plants in terrestrial ecosystems, since they too undergo photosynthesis and serve as a vital food source for other organisms.

MINERAL CYCLES

Plants are involved in mineral cycles. For example, plants get nitrogen compounds from the soil and combine them with carbohydrates to make proteins. Animals get the nitrogen compounds they need by eating plant proteins. The nitrogen returns to the soil as animal waste. Bacteria and fungi then turn the waste back into simple nitrogen compounds, which the plants can use once more.

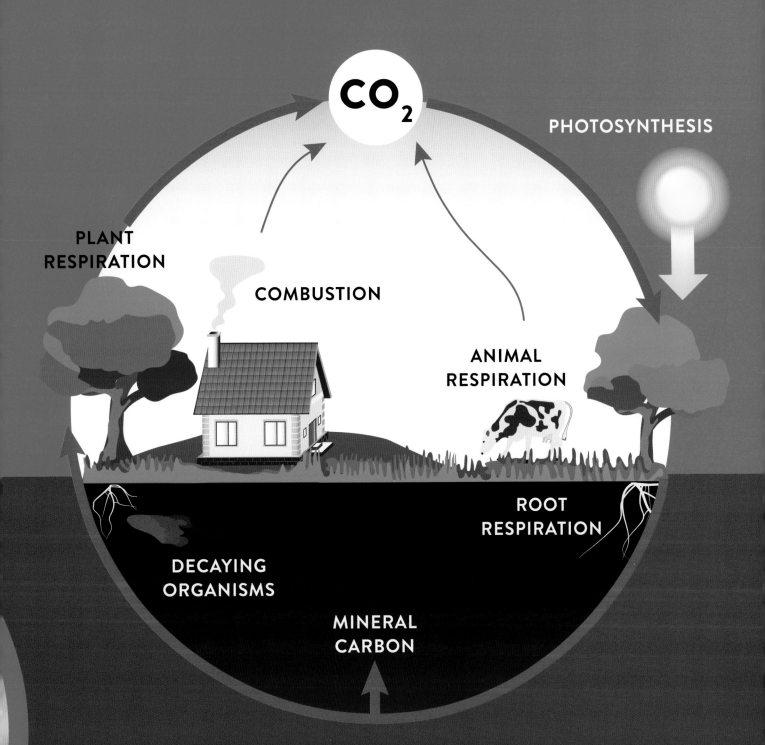

THE CARBON CYCLE

Plants play a crucial role in the nutrient cycles of ecosystems. They take in carbon dioxide from the air during photosynthesis and use it to build their own tissues. When vegetation is eaten, this organic carbon is used to build animal tissue and as a source of energy. The carbon is converted into carbon dioxide and released back into the air through respiration, the decay of animal wastes, and the decomposition of tissues after the animal's death. This exchange is called the carbon cycle.

MOSSES

Mosses are small, seedless plants that often grow in moist, shady places. More than 10,000 species, or types, of moss grow throughout the world. They belong to a group of plants called bryophytes.

WHAT ARE BRYOPHYTES?

A bryophyte is a green, seedless nonvascular plant that is one of the mosses, liverworts, or hornworts. Bryophytes are among the simplest of the terrestrial, or land-based, plants, yet they show considerable diversity in form and ecology. They are widely distributed throughout the world and are relatively small compared with most seed-bearing plants.

Peat bog

WHERE DO MOSSES GROW?

Mosses range in size from too small to see to more than 40 inches (1 meter) long. They grow closely together in thick mats. Many types of moss form velvety green carpets on forest floors. These green mosses also grow on trees and rocks. Peat, or sphagnum, mosses grow in patches in bogs, in swamps, near ponds, and in other wet places. They may be green, red, orange, or brown. Granite, or rock, mosses grow on rocks in cold regions. They are reddish brown or black.

MAKING MORE MOSS

Unlike most other plants, mosses reproduce through cells called spores, not seeds. A stalklike structure produces and releases the spores. When a spore lands on a moist surface, it grows into a low, branching structure. This structure spreads across the surface of the soil, wood, or rock. Leafy shoots grow up from this low part of the plant. These shoots produce male and female sex cells. Once two sex cells join together, they grow into a new spore-producing stalk. New moss plants also can grow from pieces of old moss plants.

Irish moss is actually algae, not moss.

LIVERWORTS

The liverworts are nonvascular plants that look like flat leaves with rounded lobes. Their name comes from their shape, which in some varieties looks like that of the human liver. Liverworts were among the first plants to colonize the land. The oldest known liverwort fossils were discovered in Argentina in rocks dated to be between 473 million and 471 million years old. Today there are more than 9,000 species of liverworts.

WHERE ARE THEY FOUND?

Liverworts are found worldwide. They tend to grow in damp places and are commonly found in tropical areas. Thallose liverworts, which are branching and ribbonlike, favor moist soil or damp rocks. Leafy liverworts are found in similar habitats, as well as on tree trunks in damp woods.

WHAT DO THEY DO?

Though not economically useful to humans, liverworts play several key roles in their ecosystems. They provide food for animals and facilitate the decay of logs. The ability of liverworts to retain moisture aids in the breakdown of rocks.

MANY KINDS

There are more than 9,000 species of these small spore-producing plants.

FERNS

Ferns are flowerless green plants. They are usually easy to recognize by the featherlike shape of their leaves, which are called fronds. Ferns reproduce by spores rather than by seeds. Some plants that are called ferns, such as asparagus ferns, reproduce by seeds and are not true ferns.

FINDING FERNS

There are about 12,000 different species, or types, of fern throughout the world. Some types first appeared on Earth more than 360 million years ago. Ferns commonly grow in tropical rainforests. They also grow in other warm, moist places where there is plenty of shade. Very few species of fern are found in dry, cold places.

Many fern species grow on the trunks and branches of trees. Others grow in bogs and marshes or float on the surface of ponds. Some types of fern, called bracken, spread like a weed through fields and pastures.

FIVE FAST FACTS

1. The smallest ferns are only a fraction of an inch tall. The largest ferns measure from 30 to 80 feet (10 to 25 meters) tall.

2. Young fern leaves are tightly curled. When they grow and begin to unfurl, they resemble the neck of a violin.

3. Ferns grow millions of spores on the underside of their leaves. These spores scatter into the air. A small number of them fall on damp surfaces and soils. They grow into tiny, kidney-shaped structures. These structures produce male and female cells, which together produce a new fern.

4. People often use ferns to decorate their homes and gardens.

5. Such animals as deer eat ferns, and some birds use them to line their nests.

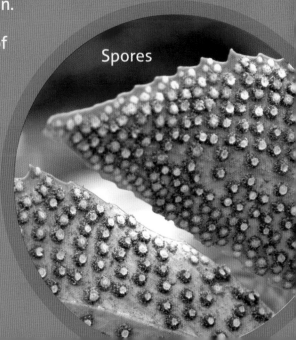

Spores

FLOWERS

Most plants pass on life to future plant generations by seeds. It is the work of a flower to make seed. All its beauty serves this one purpose. Color and perfume attract insects and hummingbirds to aid in the flower's pollination. Some flowers are so formed that they admit certain insects and no others. At least 250,000 species of flowering plants are known.

PARTS OF A FLOWER

A flower usually has four main parts. These are the calyx, the corolla, the stamens, and the pistils. All of these parts are usually bunched together at the tip, or receptacle, of the flower stem.

The calyx is the outermost part of a flower. It is made up of sepals. The sepals are usually green and look like small leaves. The sepals enclose and protect the flower bud while it is developing into a flower.

The flower's petals form the corolla. Within the corolla are the stamens and the pistils. The stamens are the male parts of a flower. They produce tiny grains called pollen. Pollen grains contain sperm cells. The pistils are the female parts of a flower. The pistils contain egg cells that can develop into seeds. Some flowers have both stamens and pistils. Others have either stamens or pistils.

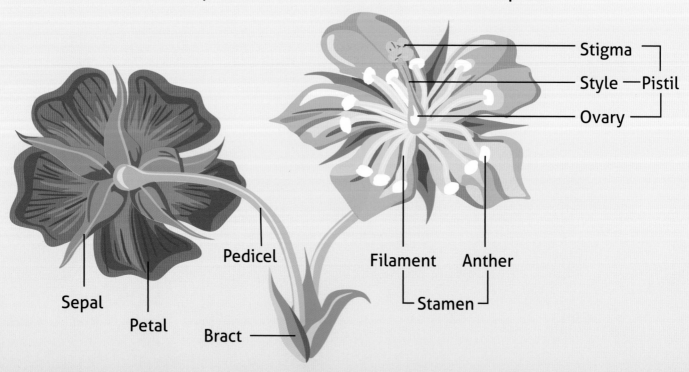

Stigma
Style — Pistil
Ovary

Pedicel

Filament   Anther
Stamen

Sepal

Petal

Bract

The most primitive modern flowers are the members of the buttercup order, Ranales.

POLLINATION

A seed cannot grow until pollen is transferred from the stamen to the pistil. This transfer is called pollination. Since flowers cannot go after pollen, they depend upon some carrier to bring it to them. Flowers are pollinated by flies, moths, wasps, bees, and sometimes by hummingbirds.

The most common flower with seeds that are readily scattered by the wind is the dandelion, regarded by most people as a weed.

GARDEN FLOWERS

All the familiar garden flowers of today have been developed from wild flowers. They were chosen for cultivation because of their beauty. By careful selection and cross-pollination of the finest plants, their blooms have been made even more beautiful. Some of them now bear little resemblance to their wild ancestors.

The hollycock came originally from China.

The wild tulip blooms from the Mediterranean eastward into Asia. Turkish gardeners were the first to collect fine specimens and develop the garden tulip.

FIVE FAST FACTS

1 About 10,000 species of plants are cultivated for their ornamental flowers alone.

2 Flowers were first cultivated for food.

3 Many flowers have been cultivated for their medicinal properties.

4 Flowers were raised for their beauty alone in ancient China, Egypt, Sumer, Babylonia, and Assyria.

5 On a worldwide basis, commercial flower growing has become a multi-billion dollar business. The enterprise became popular in the late 19th century in England and throughout Western Europe, where the growers were trained primarily in vast royal and estate gardens.

The marigold came originally from Mexico.

The chrysanthemum is the national flower of Japan.

EXPLORERS, HORTICULTURISTS, AND BREEDERS

It is the work of the plant explorer to bring material from the far places of the world and establish it in an experimental garden. The horticulturist then works on it, sometimes for many years, to develop the choice garden flowers which can be raised by the amateur. Plant breeders create new flowers. They improve flowers by two methods—hybridizing and crossbreeding. The basic objective is to combine in one individual plant the desirable characteristics found in different plants. Larger blossoms, new colors, longer and earlier blooming periods, resistance to disease, greater hardiness in northern climates, and more attractive plant forms are some of the characteristics developed by hybridizing.

In Elizabethan England, violets were eaten raw with onions and lettuce or mixed in broth.

WILD FLOWERS

The native flowering plants of a region are its wild flowers. They originated there and grow wild year after year under natural conditions if they are undisturbed by humans.

Rafflesia

GROUPS OF PLANTS

Plants live in groups because of their similar needs. Some grow in forests, others on the open prairies. The sides of streams and the mud bottoms of ponds also have their flower communities.

WHERE ARE THEY FOUND?

Wild flowers have been found blooming in the Arctic, on high mountains, and even at the edges of glaciers. They cover the deserts in a riot of color after a heavy rain. Immense and gorgeous blooms grow in the tropics. The greatest variety of wild flowers is found in the temperate zone. Here each flower blooms in its proper season according to the laws of its nature.

The Virginia bluebell is a popular spring-blooming garden and wild flower that is native to moist woods and wet meadows in eastern North America.

FIVE FAST FACTS

① The largest flower in the world is the reddish or purplish brown rafflesia of Malaya. It measures up to 3 feet (1 meter) across and weighs about 15 pounds (7 kilograms).

② The smallest is the duckweed, no larger than a tack head.

③ Sometimes wildflowers that grow naturally in a certain area are not originally from that area. For example, nearly all bright flowers that grow on the islands of Hawaii came from other parts of the tropics and subtropics.

④ Some wild flowers that grow in the forests store up food in bulbs and rootstocks, so they do not need long hours of sunshine.

⑤ Flowers are saved, together with other forms of wildlife, by the establishment of national, state, and local parks, forests, and sanctuaries.

Rosemary

HERBS

Herbs are the fragrant leaves or other parts of certain plants. These plants are also known as herbs. Common herbs include mint, basil, oregano, bay, parsley, and thyme. People use herbs, dried or fresh, to add flavor and aroma to foods. Herbs are also used in some cosmetics, teas, and medicines.

WHERE ARE THEY FOUND?

Most herbs grow in mild climates. However, herbs can be planted wherever the growing conditions are good. Many people grow herbs indoors. In general, herbs grow well in dry, well-drained soil. Many require a lot of sunlight. Natural fertilizers, such as manure or compost, help herbs to form the oils that give them their flavor.

PLANT PARTS

Most herbs come from the leaves of a plant. Bay leaves come from an evergreen tree called the bay laurel. Rosemary and sage are the leaves of bushes. Some herbs come from other parts of a plant. Ginseng comes from the roots of ginseng plants. All parts of the fennel plant can be used as flavoring.

Basil plant

Dried thyme

Fennel

HERBS IN HISTORY

People have used herbs for thousands of years. Early doctors used herbs to treat many illnesses. By the Middle Ages (about AD 500 to 1500), many Europeans were using herbs in their cooking. When the first settlers came from Europe to North America, they brought these herbs with them. Native Americans taught the settlers about the herbs growing in the Americas.

WEEDS

According to the common definition, a weed is any plant growing where it is not wanted. Any tree, vine, shrub, or herb may qualify as a weed, depending on the situation. Generally, however, the term is reserved for those plants whose vigorous, invasive habits of growth pose a serious threat to desirable, cultivated plants.

One individual pigweed, a common annual weed, may produce 117,400 seeds in a single year.

WEED OR CROP?

One person's weed may be another's prized crop. The most dramatic example of this is the common dandelion. To the suburban homeowner this deep-rooted wildflower may be nothing more than a pest, an unsightly blight in the lawn. Yet nutritionists prize dandelion greens as a rich source of vitamins A and C.

The seed capsules of the cocklebur use hooked prickles to attach themselves to the fur of passing animals and ride to new territory.

WEEDS VS. USEFUL PLANTS

Although a stalk of crabgrass or a tendril of wild morning glory may seem insignificant, plant pests such as these can reduce crop yields by as much as 10 percent. Through competition for light, moisture, minerals, and soil, a weed robs cultivated plants of vital resources. Weeds pose other threats as well. The effect of ragweed pollen on hay fever sufferers is common knowledge; less well known is the role weeds play as hosts to harmful insects and diseases.

CAN WEEDS BE GOOD?

Weeds may benefit the environment in a number of ways. They help to invigorate poor or exhausted soils, adding humus as they decompose. By sheltering the soil from the sun and wind, weeds actually promote the germination of other, less rugged plants. Birds, rodents, and many other kinds of wildlife depend on weeds for the berries and seeds they furnish. Animals also find shelter in the cover provided by the weeds' foliage.

Plant botanists use the term pioneers to describe the species that first colonize disturbed habitats, lands stripped bare by natural catastrophes or by human exploitation. The colorful perennial known as fireweed earned its name for the speed with which it follows in the wake of forest fires.

Water lilies

WATER PLANTS

The diverse members of the enormous group of plants known as water plants, or hydrophytes, have adapted remarkably well to their life in the water. Many of the plants retain common structures that indicate that all hydrophytes originated on land.

ADAPTING TO THE WATER

These specialized flowering plants live in or on the water either wholly or partially submerged. Most have adapted to their watery environments by developing conspicuous air passages, such as are seen in the stalks of water lilies or caladiums. These passages transport the necessary air to the plant's underwater parts and increase the plant's buoyancy. The roots in most cases are much reduced. They serve chiefly as anchors, not for extracting food as their terrestrial counterparts do. In some cases the roots have disappeared entirely, and many water plants float throughout their existence.

A duck swims in duckweed.

FREE FLOATING

There are three distinct types of water plants. The first type is made up of the free-floating societies. Their plants are entirely supported by water and move freely. In this group are the algae and duckweeds. They float in stagnant or slow-moving water.

PONDWEED

The pondweed societies are anchored, but their bodies may be submerged or floating. Here belong seaweeds, often with elaborate holdfasts, or suckerlike disks; water lilies, with broad floating leaves; and pondweeds, or pickerel weeds, with submerged leaves.

SWAMP SOCIETIES

The third type of water plants is made up of the many swamp societies. The plants are rooted in water or in soil rich in water, but their leaf-bearing stems rise above the surface. In this group are included the cattail marshes, sphagnum moss swamps, alder and willow thickets, and forests of tamarack (larch) and other water-loving trees.

Pickerel weed

Cattail marsh

TREES

Trees are tall woody plants that regularly renew their growth. Most plants classified as trees have one main trunk, or stem, that contains woody tissues. In most species the trunk produces secondary limbs, called branches. The stem often has no branches for several feet above the ground. At the top it may have a crown of branches and leaves. Most trees grow to 15 feet (4.5 meters) or more in height, and some are much taller. Shrubs are smaller. They branch close to the ground and have many stems.

THREE MAIN PARTS

A tree has three main parts. The roots anchor it in the ground. They absorb water and dissolve minerals. The trunk and branches carry a watery fluid known as sap and hold the leaves in the sunlight. The leaves make food.

CAMBIUM

Between the bark and the wood is a layer of cells called cambium. Cambium is perpetually youthful tissue. The cells at the tip of every twig grow just like cells in a newly sprouted seedling.

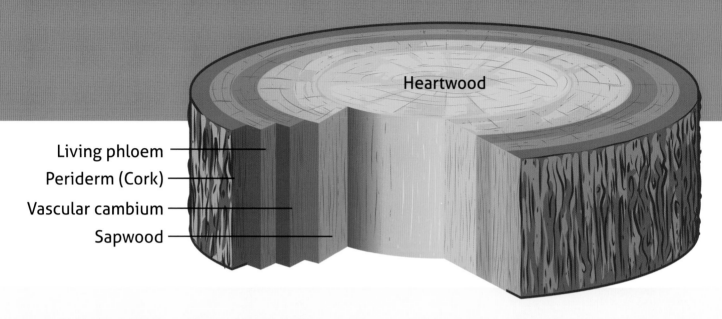

Heartwood

Living phloem
Periderm (Cork)
Vascular cambium
Sapwood

COUNTING THE RINGS

A tree grows higher and wider as its twigs and branches lengthen at the tips. Meanwhile the branches, twigs, and trunk grow thicker. Conifers and most deciduous trees add thickness. Every year the cambium adds a layer of new cells to the older wood. Each layer forms a ring. By counting the rings one can tell the age of the tree. They are thick in years of good rainfall and thin in poor years. Tree rings give a clue to climatic conditions in past centuries.

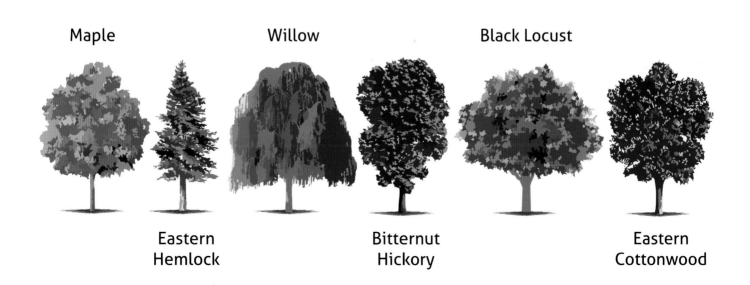

Maple

Willow

Black Locust

Eastern
Hemlock

Bitternut
Hickory

Eastern
Cottonwood

Botanists divide trees into two main groups, called coniferous and broad-leaved. Those in the first group bear cones and usually have needle-shaped leaves. Among them are the pine, hemlock, spruce, redwood, cedar, and cypress. Most conifers keep their leaves all year, and those that do are called evergreens. Trees of the second group have broad, flat leaves. Most of them shed their leaves in winter and are therefore called deciduous. The oak, maple, elm, beech, ash, linden, sycamore, and willow are common deciduous trees.

Bristletone pine, a conifer

FIVE FAST FACTS

① Conifers grow cones to reproduce instead of flowers or fruits.

② Conifers are found in all parts of the world where trees grow. They are most abundant in cool regions, where they are important timber trees and ornamentals.

③ Some of the oldest, tallest, and heaviest types of trees are conifers. Among the oldest living things on Earth, the bristlecone pines of desert mountains in California and Nevada commonly live for 3,000 to 4,000 years.

④ A conifer, the redwood of coastal California is the world's tallest tree, with some redwoods growing to more than 360 feet (110 meters) in height.

⑤ Conifers provide all of the world's softwood timber, the major construction wood of temperate regions.

Redwood, a conifer

TREES HELP THE LAND

The roots of trees keep soil from washing or blowing away. Leaf mold adds richness to soil. Thick mats of leaves and roots on the ground soak up rainwater and keep it from draining rapidly into streams and rivers.

Willow, a deciduous tree

Linden, a deciduous tree

PALMS

Among the most useful of all plants, palms furnish food, shelter, clothing, fuel, building materials, starch, oils, and a host of minor products for peoples of the tropics. There are about 2,780 species of palms. They grow in the form of trees, shrubs, and vines and occur primarily in tropical or subtropical climates, though some grow in temperate regions. By far the largest number of palms are found in tropical America (with about 500 species concentrated in Brazil alone) and tropical Asia.

EUCALYPTUS

Next to the Douglas fir and the giant redwoods of the American West, the tallest tree in the world is the giant gum of Australia, which grows to more than 300 feet (90 meters) high. There are more than 500 species of eucalyptus trees, or eucalypts. They are native to Australia (including Tasmania) and nearby islands. The leaves of some species secrete an oil that is extracted by steam distillation to furnish the eucalyptus oil used to make expectorants and inhalants in medicine.

CYPRESS

One of the most durable of all woods, cypress resists insects and chemical corrosion as well as decay and has a smell resembling that of cedar. The Italian cypress is a tall evergreen of Mediterranean shores. It yields wood that lasts for centuries.

GIANT SEQUOIA

Giant sequoias are among the oldest of the forest trees, living for 3,000 years or more. Also called the big tree or Sierra redwood, the giant sequoia reaches heights of more than 280 feet (85 meters) and may have a maximum trunk diameter of more than 25 feet (8 meters).

General Sherman, a sequoia found in Sequoia National Park

EXTREME PLANTS

SURVIVING THE HEAT

Plants that are able to survive hot, dry climates are called xerophytes. Xerophytes have a wide variety of adaptations to conserve water. For example, most plants that grow in deserts have thick waxy cuticles on the outer surfaces of their leaves to minimize water loss. In many desert plants, such as cacti, leaves may be absent altogether. In such plants photosynthesis is carried out in the outer tissues of the thick, fleshy stems. Many cacti have extensive shallow roots. When it rains, these roots can take up large quantities of water very quickly. This water is stored in the central core of the stems. Cacti can survive in the desert for years on the water gathered from a single rainfall.

The ocotillo of the southwestern United States and Mexico resembles a bunch of dead sticks most of the time. Following a rain, however, it quickly produces leaves that begin making food. Within a few weeks, the plant produces flowers. When its seeds mature, the ocotillo loses its leaves and becomes dormant again.

QUICK GERMINATION

Many annual desert plants germinate only after heavy rain. They quickly grow, flower, and produce seeds. The parent plant then dies and the seeds are deposited in the soil. These seeds are very resistant to heat and drought and remain dormant in the soil until the next heavy rain.

SURVIVING THE COLD

Plants that grow in the Arctic or on high mountain slopes must be able to endure severe cold and very short growing seasons. These plants have specialized cell structures that prevent damage from ice-crystal formation. In addition, many of these species are able to carry out life processes at unusually cold temperatures. Many Arctic grasses, for example, photosynthesize best at temperatures very near the freezing point.

Arctic vegetation

Golden barrel cactus

CACTI

Cactuses, or cacti, are desert plants. They grow in dry places where other plants have trouble living. Their ability to store water keeps them alive. Cacti are also protected by sharp spines, or needles. These discourage animals from eating them.

WHERE CACTI GROW

There are about 1,650 species of cactus. These plants grow mainly in the dry areas of the United States, Mexico, Central America, and South America. Mexico has the greatest number and variety of cacti.

STORING WATER

Cacti are succulent plants. This means that they have thick tissues that take up and hold large amounts of water. The stored water keeps them alive during dry periods. Unlike many plants, cacti do not have deep roots. Instead they have roots that spread out near the surface of the soil. This is important to their survival. These roots absorb water from a wide area during the few times it rains.

HOW BIG ARE THEY?

Cacti come in many sizes. The cactus called the prickly pear grows in low bunches. The giant cactus known as the saguaro can be 50 feet (15 meters) tall. Its branches may be 2 feet (about 0.6 meter) thick.

Saguaros

USES

Cacti are often grown for decoration. Many unusual and beautiful varieties are prized as houseplants. In South America cacti are sometimes used as fences. Some types of cacti are also grown for food. The egg-shaped fruit of the saguaro can be eaten. People also eat the fruit of the prickly pear.

A bird eats the fruit from a saguaro cactus.

Prickly pear

BOTANY

Plants are found throughout the world, on land, in water, and even hanging from other plants in the air. They are extremely important organisms, essential to the continuation of all life on Earth. Because of both their crucial role and their own interesting variations, plants are the subjects of the science of botany.

A WIDE FIELD

Botany is the study of not only the so-called vascular plants, such as garden flowers, vines, shrubs, and trees, but also of nonvascular plants, such as mosses and ferns. It also traditionally includes the study of algae, fungi, and bacteria, organisms that were formerly considered to be plants.

TYPES OF BOTANY

Botanists usually focus on a specific area. Some discover new kinds of plants, name them, and classify them (group them with similar plants). Other botanists study the structure and form of plants. Many botanists work as researchers. Some researchers study plant diseases. Others experiment with plant chemicals. Others try to develop plants that are more useful to humans. Many botanists are interested in conservation. Some investigate the effects of pollution on plants. Others work to protect rare plants.

DIOSCORIDES

THEOPHRASTVS

THE FIRST BOTANISTS

No written record exists of any scientific botany before the time of Aristotle in the 4th century BC. Theophrastus, a student of Aristotle, is credited with founding botany. He wrote the *De historia plantarum*, an early classification of the known plants of the world. Four hundred years later, another Greek, Pedanius Dioscorides, wrote the *De materia medica*, which describes the medicinal uses of many plants.

HUMANS AND PLANTS

Humans are dependent upon plants. Directly or indirectly, plants provide food, clothing, fuel, shelter, and many other necessities of life. Humankind's dependence on crops such as wheat and corn (maize) is obvious, but without grass and grain, the livestock that provide people with food and other animal products could not survive either.

Oat field

FOOD

Starches and sugars, the foods that plants make and store for their own growth, are also the fundamental nutrients that humans and other organisms need in order to live. In North America the chief food plants are cereal grains. Major cereal crops include corn, wheat, oats, rice, barley, and rye. Legumes are the second greatest source of plant-based food in North America. Legumes such as peas, dry beans, soybeans, and peanuts are high in protein and oil. Seasonings and many beverages come from plants and plant materials, too.

Cotton field

CLOTHING

Much human clothing is made from material that comes directly from plants. Cotton is the principal plant used for clothing manufacture.

An artisan makes paper.

PAPER

More than 4,500 years ago, the ancient Egyptians prepared the first paper from the fibrous stems of papyrus, a grasslike plant. About AD 100 the Chinese invented a method of manufacturing paper that is still used today.

SHELTER

Shelter in many parts of the world is made from wood. Plant materials appear in a number of places in human dwellings. Furniture is commonly composed of wood and cloth made from plant fibers.

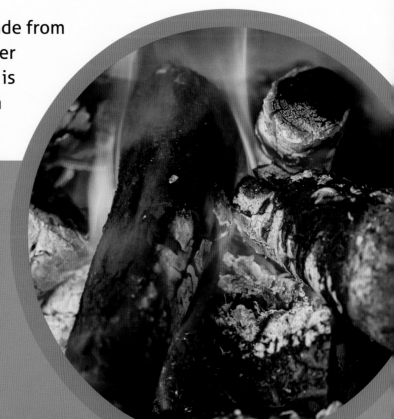

FUEL

Coal and natural gas are fuels used for heating and cooking. Each had their origin in plants and other organisms that lived on Earth long ago. Wood is still burned for heat in many parts of the world, and it is popular for use in open fireplaces.

MEDICINE

Through the ages, people have found that certain plants could be used to relieve their aches and pains. Most medicine men and physicians in ancient cultures were experts on plants. In fact, the study of botany in Europe and America had its beginnings in medicine, when doctors searched for herbs to cure disease.

YESTERDAY AND TODAY

Many medicinal plants that were discovered by early peoples are still in use today. For example, some Native Americans chewed on the leaves of willows to relieve aches and pains. These leaves contain salicylic acid, a compound very similar to aspirin. The leaves of the foxglove yield digitalis, which is used to treat heart disease. Quinine, from the bark of the South American cinchona tree, was long used to combat malaria.

Willow leaves

Foxglove

Cinchona bark

Periwinkle

NEW DISCOVERIES

Medicinal substances are still being discovered in plants. Vincristine, a medicine that has proved effective in the treatment of leukemia in children, was discovered in the common periwinkle plant. The periwinkle is native to South Africa and is cultivated in gardens around the world. Many plants are invaluable sources of vitamins, whose importance to human growth and health was an important 20th-century discovery.

DANGEROUS PLANTS

Not all drugs derived from plants are beneficial. Some plant drugs are violent poisons or habit-forming narcotics. These include peyote, which is derived from a cactus, and opium, which comes from a poppy.

TEST WHAT YOU KNOW

1. **How many plant species have been identified?**
   Less than 90,000
   Between 100,000 and 125,000
   More than 300,000

2. **This material lends stiffness to stems and twigs.**
   Cellulose
   Chlorophyll
   Glucose

3. **Biennials produce blossoms in this year.**
   First year
   Second year

4. **Hornworts are seedless vascular plants.**
   True
   False

5. **Which statement is true?**
   Xylem carries water, while phloem carries sugary sap.
   Xylem carries sugary sap, while phloem carries water.

6. **Which statement explains why leaves change colors?**
   A rising level of chlorophyll as a plant prepares for winter.
   A decreasing level of chlorophyll allows other pigments to show.

7. **Ferns reproduce by this method.**
   Spores
   Seeds

8. **This term describes plants that grow in water.**
   Xerophytes
   Hydrophytes